Maths
made easy

Preschool
ages 3-5
Workbook 4

Author and Consultant
Su Hurrell

LONDON • NEW YORK • SYDNEY • MOSCOW • DELHI

Not the same

Draw a (ring) round the animal that is not the same.

Draw **2** animals not the same.

Not the same

Draw a (ring) round the sock that is different.

Draw a (ring) round the glove that is different.

Draw a sock that is different.   Draw a glove that is different.

Different

Draw a (ring) round the flag that is different.

Draw the flag that is different.

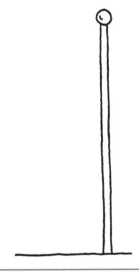

Draw what it should look like.

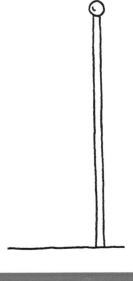

Different numbers

Count how many spots on the big ladybird.

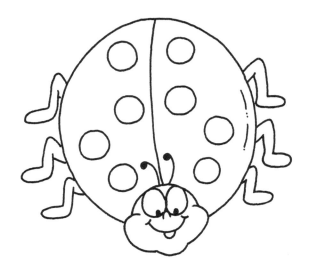

Draw a ⟨ring⟩ round the ladybird with
a different number of spots.

Draw a ⟨ring⟩ round the ladybird with
a different number of spots.

Different numbers

Draw a different number of shapes on the umbrellas.

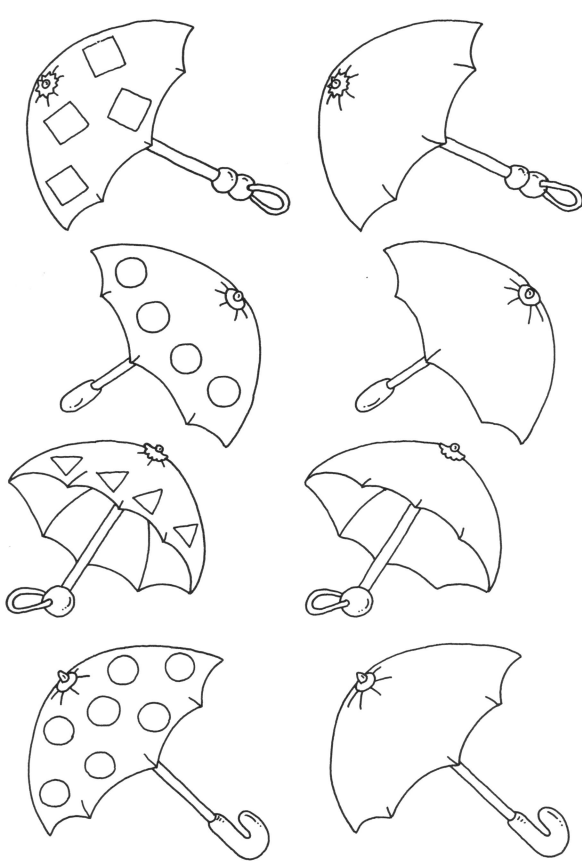

The same

Match the animals.

Draw and colour **2** animals the same.

The same

Draw lines to match the shoes that are the same. Make pairs.

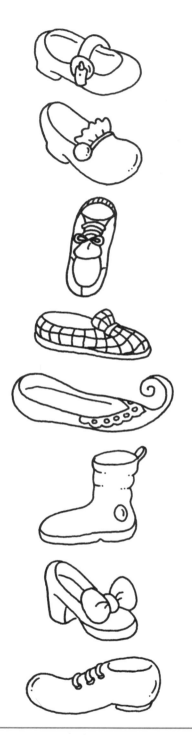

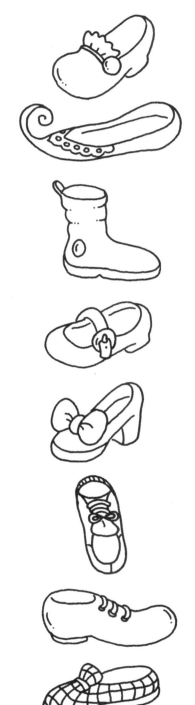

Draw a pair of shoes for yourself.

The same

Find the big circles O. Colour them yellow.
Find the big triangles △. Colour them red.

Find the small circles ○. Colour them blue.
Find the small triangles ▵ colour them green

How many green triangles

Count how many red triangles.

How many yellow circles

Count how many blue circles.

The same

Draw lines to match the monsters.

The same

Draw the other half to match.
Use a mirror to help you.

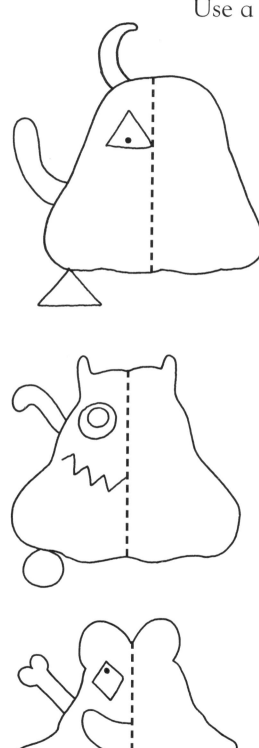

Sorting sets

Draw a line to the right set.

Count how
many altogether.

Count how
many altogether.

Count how
many altogether.

Count how
many altogether.

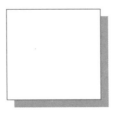

Adding to sets

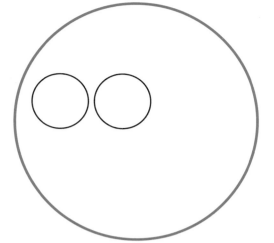

Draw **2** more.
Count how many
in the set.

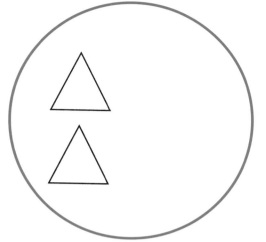

Draw **1** more.
Count how many
in the set.

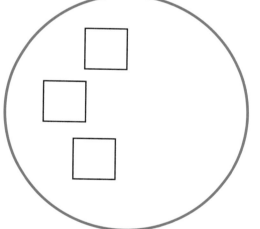

Draw **3** more.
Count how many
in the set.

Draw **4** more.
Count how many
in the set.

Draw a set of **6** triangles.

Sorting the toys

Look at the toys in the circles.
Match the other toys to the right circle.

Sorting the trees

Count how many apples on each tree.

How many trees have...

3 apples	

4 apples	

5 apples	

Draw 1 more tree for each set.

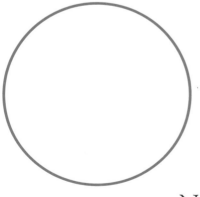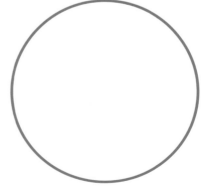

Now how many trees have...

3 apples	

4 apples	

5 apples	

Sorting the animals

Look at the animals. Count how many legs.
Match them to the right part of the Ark.

Notes for parents

During play activities, children frequently match, sort, create patterns, and talk about sequences. This book reinforces and establishes those concepts and skills in a fun and enjoyable way.

The book includes some counting and number matching, so your child should be familiar with the numbers and quantities up to 10. Shapes and colours are also included in some activities.

Content
By working through this book your child will learn:
• to look closely at shapes, objects, and patterns;
• to match;
• to identify similarities and differences;
• to sort things into sets;
• to use more than one criterion for this sorting process;
• to add to sets and count the total;
• to recognise what a pattern is;
• to continue patterns and create them;
• to understand the concept of before and after;
• to put events in the right sequential order;
• to use ordinal numbers correctly;
• to complete sequences.

How to help your child
A child learns through hands-on experiences so it is important your child has had a range of practical experiences before attempting the activities in the book.

This book is designed to be an enjoyable experience for both you and your child, a shared time together. Make sure that your child is alert and not too tired. Keep the time spent appropriate to the age and level of concentration of your child.

The pages are designed for your child to colour, which develops pencil control, eye and hand co-ordination and builds up concentration. Make sure there is a range of coloured pencils or felt-tip pens available.

Talk about the activities on each page and make sure your child understands what they are to do.

Remember this book is for fun as well as being educational, so stop before your child loses concentration or is restless. This will ensure they want to come back for more!

How to use the book

The same/different

Before attempting the first 10 pages of the book, play matching games with your child. Match shoes, socks, plates, or fruit, concentrating on what is the same and what is different about them.

Talk about things that match.

Talk about what is the same and what is different. Encourage your child to notice small differences as well as the obvious ones. For instance, in a collection of leaves, some may be pointed, others may be round, some rough and others smooth.

This will develop their skill of observation. This skill is helpful in early reading, to differentiate the shapes of letters and how they contribute to words, and in other curriculum areas such as science and art.

Sorting

Sorting is a very practical activity, so make sure that your child has many sorting opportunities before doing these pages. Your child can sort the toys at tidying up time, sort the washing, sort the shopping into tins or packets.

Categories or criteria have been used to enable sorting to be both meaningful and useful in everyday life. The pages introduce various criteria which are set in appropriate contexts for your child.

Observation and counting are skills that the child will revisit.

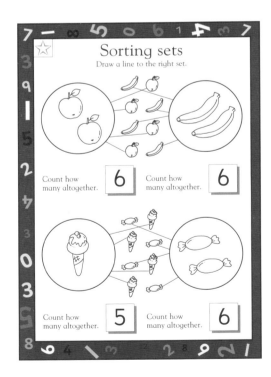

Patterns

Recognising and creating patterns is both fun and an important aspect of a child's development. Later they will be expected to see patterns in numbers and in science results, as well as to recognise the creative element of making patterns.

Before doing the pages talk to your child about patterns that they see all around them. They will probably be on fabric, wallpaper, kitchenware, and in books.

At first let your child copy patterns you have made, with buttons, beads, cups, or even small toys, and then encourage them to make their own. Keep them simple at first, perhaps using just two colours: red button, blue button, red button. As your child becomes more confident, encourage them to create more complex patterns.

It is fun to create your own patterns by printing with corks, small boxes, or with fingers and hands.

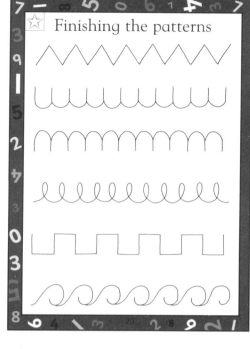

Sequencing

Sequencing and getting things in the right order can be difficult for the young child.

Give your child the opportunity to experience the order or sequence of actions and events within the context of their daily life. Talk about what they do before and after something, and what comes next. Introduce words such as first, second, and third.

Write the numbers 1–10 on some cards and encourage your child to put them in the right order.

3

Page-by-page notes

Page 2 – Not the same

Your child has to choose the animals that are the same and draw a ring around the animal that is not the same.

At the bottom of the page your child can choose to draw any two animals that are not the same. Talk about their choice.

Page 3 – Not the same

Once again the activity is to encourage your child to find the object that is not the same.

Your child can then draw a sock and a glove that are different from the ones shown on the page.

Page 4 – Different

This page uses the concept of 'different' on its own; the child should by now understand that 'different' means 'not the same'. The child has to draw a ring around the flag that is different, as well as draw the two flags.

Page 5 – Different numbers

This page reinforces the concept of different numbers through the comparison of spots on ladybirds.

Page 6 – Different numbers

The child can count the shapes on the umbrellas and then draw a different amount on the umbrellas opposite.

Page 7 – The same

The child has to identify matching animals. Encourage your child to draw the line starting on the left, moving to the right. This reinforces the left to right movement needed for writing and reading. At the bottom of the page your child can choose the animals they want to draw.

Page 8 – The same

This page introduces the word 'pair'. Talk to your child about pairs – two of a kind that go together. In the second activity, your child can draw a pair of shoes.

Page 9 – The same

This page encourages your child to look at both the size and the type of shape. If they are not sure of their colours they may need your help to complete this task.

They also have to count the number of shapes coloured in a specific colour.

Page 10 – The same

This is a fun page where your child has to match the monsters.

Page 11 – The same

The child has to draw the other half of the monster to match. If it is appropriate, talk to your child about halves. 'Half' is introduced in this context as 'the other half,' which also implies symmetry. Have fun looking for other objects that are symmetrical, buttons, letters, for example. Children can use a mirror to help them see the other half.

Page 12 – Sorting sets

The word 'set' is used instead of group as it is a word with which your child should become familiar before starting school.

On this page the activities involve sorting things into sets by drawing a line to the appropriate set ring, and then counting how many there are in that set.

When your child writes the numbers make sure that they start at the top and that there are no reversals.

Page 13 – Adding to sets

Your child should add to the sets by drawing as many more shapes as asked for and should then count how many in the set.

Page 14 – Sorting the toys

For this activity there are two set rings, one with wheeled toys and the other with toys without wheels. Talk to your child about the toys in the sets. What do they notice? They are all toys, but what is the difference between the two sets? What is the same about the toys in each set?

After you have talked about what your child notices, encourage them to do the sorting. An example is given for each set.

Page 15 – Sorting the trees

Talk about the page and then let your child do the sorting. For this task your child has to sort the trees according to the number of apples in them. Count how many of each tree. Your child has to draw an additional tree with the requisite number of apples. Now count how many of each type of tree including those drawn by the child.

Page 16 – Sorting the animals

In this activity your child has to sort the animals according to the number of legs and draw a line to the right part of the Ark. An example has been shown.

Page 17 – Sorting the animals

This time the animals with the same number of legs, as specified, have to be ringed.

Page 18 – Sorting the fish

This is both a sorting and a matching activity. Your child has to look at the number on each fish and match that fish to the fisherman wearing that number. They should draw a fishing line for each fish that matches.

Page 19 – Sorting the fish

This too is a sorting and a matching activity. Your child has to look closely at the patterns on the fish and match each fish to the fisherman wearing a hat with the same pattern. They should draw a fishing line for each fish that matches. Children may like to use a different colour for each number.

At the bottom of the page the child has to count how many fish there are of each pattern.

Page 20 – Finishing the patterns

This page encourages your child to finish simple patterns that have been started for them. Left to right movement is important. The first four patterns are the basis for letters.

Page 21 – Finishing the patterns

Your child has to complete patterns and create their own.

This activity can be extended beyond the book and your child can decorate their own paper plates.

Page 22 – Finishing the patterns

Again your child has to complete the patterns. The repeating is simple but make sure your child really looks at the items; some involve counting.

Page 23 – Finishing the patterns

These are more complex, so make sure your child understands what they are to do.

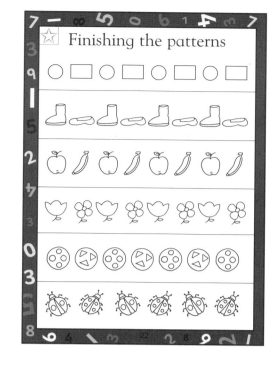

Page 24 – In the right order

This page relates to a child's world and what they do before and after something.

Talk about the pictures before your child puts the ticks in the boxes. Also talk about the pictures illustrating first, second, and third before completing the boxes.

Page 25 – In the right order

The activities involve three pictures and your child has to decide what comes first, second or third in the sequence of events.

Talk about the pictures before your child completes the task.

Page 26 – The missing number

Here your child has to complete the sequence of numbers by drawing the missing objects.

If your child finds it difficult to count in twos, they may need some help with the last activity.

Page 27 – The missing numbers

In these activities there is more than one missing number.

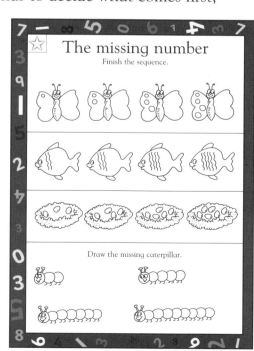

Page 28 – Mary sorted her snails

Your child will have fun matching, looking for patterns, and looking for similarities and differences in Mary's garden.

Children have to sort the different kinds of snails, draw them in the circles given, and count how many snails there are in each circle.

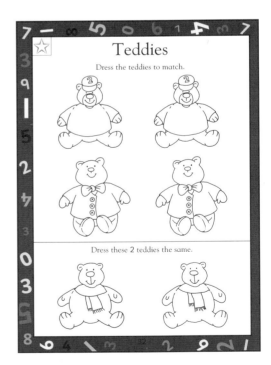

Mary sorted her snails

Sort the snails and draw them in the circles.

Count how many in each circle.

4   5   3

Page 29 – Mary grew some flowers

This page is also an exercise in matching and looking for similarities and differences.

Page 30 – The maze

Your child has to follow the pattern sequence to find their way out of the maze.

Page 31 – Dot-to-dot

By finishing the pattern and completing the dot-to-dot your child will produce lovely pictures.

At the bottom of the page they can then draw their own dot-to-dot pattern.

Page 32 – Teddies

This page is a fun page! The teddy on the right has to be dressed so that it matches the teddy on the left.

At the bottom of the page the child has to dress the teddies the same, using their imagination.

Teddies

Dress the teddies to match.

Dress these 2 teddies the same.

Sorting the animals

Count how many legs.
(Ring) the animals with the same number.

a lion   a bird   a sheep   a fish

4 legs

a fish   a duck   a ladybird   a cat

6 legs

a giraffe   a bird   a lion   a sheep

2 legs

an elephant   a fish   a bird   a mouse

0 legs

Sorting the fish

Match the fish to the fishermen.

Sorting the fish

Match the fish to the fishermen.

Count how many fish.

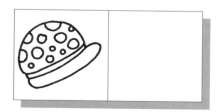

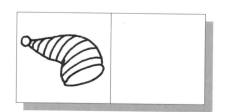

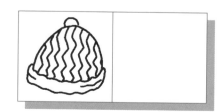

 Finishing the patterns

Finishing the patterns

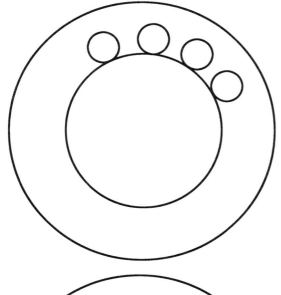

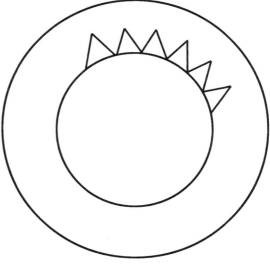

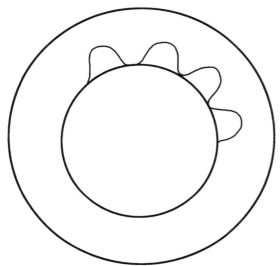

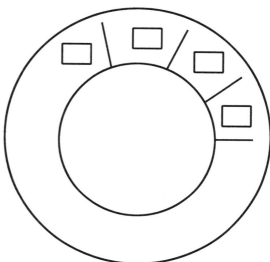

Draw your own patterns.

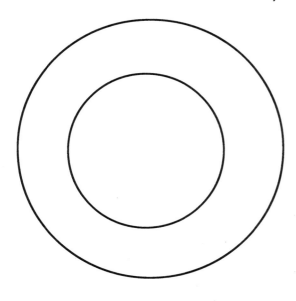

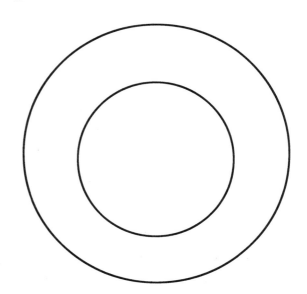

Finishing the patterns

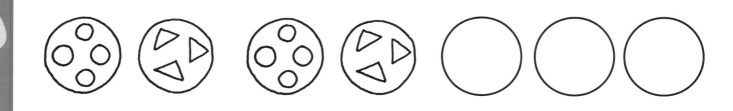

Finishing the patterns

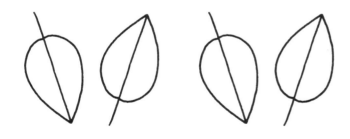

1	2	1	2				

6	7	8	6	7	8			

In the right order

✔ before

☐ ☐

✔ after

☐ ☐

Write 1st 2nd 3rd in the boxes.

☐ ☐ ☐

In the right order

Talk about the pictures.
Write 1st 2nd 3rd in the right boxes.

Talk about the pictures.
Write 1st 2nd 3rd in the right boxes.

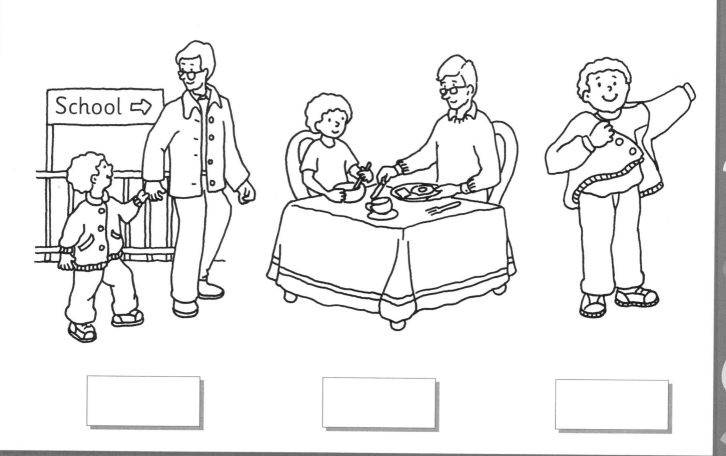

The missing number

Finish the sequence.

Finish the sequence.

Finish the sequence.

Draw the missing caterpillar.

The missing numbers

Write the missing numbers.

Write the missing numbers.

Write the missing numbers.

Mary sorted her snails

Sort the snails and draw them in the circles.

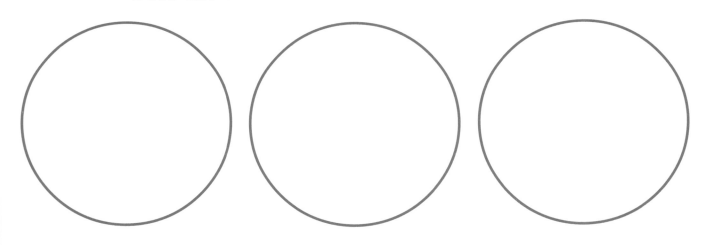

Count how many in each circle.

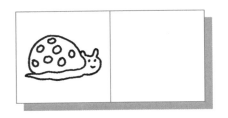
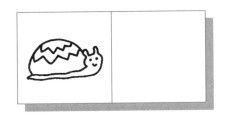

Mary grew some flowers

Draw a (ring) round the odd one out.

Draw a flower the same.

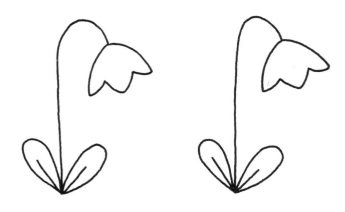

The maze

Follow the pattern to find your way out.

Dot-to-dot

Finish the patterns.

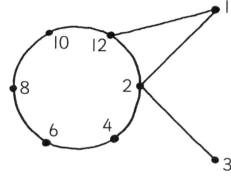

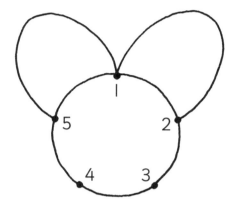

Draw your own dot-to-dot pattern.

Teddies

Dress the teddies to match.

Dress these **2** teddies the same.